A MEDIEVAL TOWN WAS A PLACE OF BUYING AND SELLING, OF CONTINUAL COMINGS AND GOINGS. THE STREETS WERE NARROW AND BUSY, WITH THE CALLS OF MERCHANTS AND THE SOUND OF CHURCH BELLS RINGING THROUGH THE TOWN.

THINKERS OF THE DAY BELIEVED THEIR SOCIETY WAS DIVIDED
INTO THREE CLASSES — THOSE WHO PRAY, THOSE WHO FIGHT
AND THOSE WHO WORK. TOWNSPEOPLE RANGED FROM THE
LOWLIEST PEASANTS TO HIGH AND POWERFUL FIGURES,
SUCH AS THE PIOUS MONKS AND HAUGHTY NOBLEMEN.

PEASANT

CISTERCIAN
MONK

YEOMAN

LORD OF
MISRULE

MERCHANT

MONK

Peasant

Peasants were the poorest people in the social pecking order. In exchange for a place to live, they worked the land to grow crops for their families and their lord.

Cistercian Monk

Cistercian monks set out to live a life faithful to the 'Rule of St Benedict' — desiring a balance between prayer and work and to be separated from town life.

Yeoman

A yeoman was a peasant who rose in social influence through the acquisition of land. He was trained in arms and fought in battle on behalf of his lord.

Lord of Misrule

During the festival of the Feast of Fools, the hierarchy of the town was reversed and a Lord of Misrule was chosen to oversee the celebrations.

Merchant

Merchants would travel from place to place selling essential and sometimes exotic goods to the people of the town.

Monk

Monks in medieval times gave up their material possessions and chose to live their lives working under the strict routine and discipline of the monastery.

LIFE FOR PEASANTS WAS A GRUELLING EXISTENCE. MANY OF THE MEN WORKED AS FARMERS IN FIELDS OWNED BY NOBLEMEN AND THEIR LIVES WERE CONTROLLED BY THE FARMING YEAR. WOMEN WERE EXPECTED TO HELP THEIR HUSBANDS WITH THE DAILY CHORES AS WELL AS PROVIDING MEALS AND RAISING CHILDREN.

In medieval times, a knight on horseback was a respected figure, symbolising honour and military power. The chivalric code was based upon strong religious ideals, willingness to defend the weak, love of one's country, loyalty to truth and, most importantly, good conquering evil.

NOBLEMAN

VILLEIN

FALCONER

BARON AND OUTLAW

NURSE AND NOBLE BOY

MINSTREL

Nobleman

A nobleman's role was to provide work, land and protection to the peasants while offering funding and military service to the monarchy.

Villein

A villein was a peasant who was bound to a lord. They worked on the land of their masters for their entire life.

Falconer

Falconry was the popular sport of hunting small wild birds with trained birds of prey. It was the falconer's job to train the hunting birds.

Nurse and Noble Boy

Noble children were often cared for by their nurses until they reached seven years old. They were then sent to another castle to continue their education.

Baron and Outlaw

Barons were wealthy men who owned land, set taxes and enforced their own justice system. An outlaw was a criminal who was no longer allowed the protection of the law.

Minstrel

Minstrels provided entertainment by singing and playing musical instruments. Their songs would record the deeds of heroic knights or of courtly love.

YEOMEN AND FRANKLINS WERE FREE MEN WHO OWNED
LAND BUT WERE NOT OF NOBLE BIRTH. THEY WOULD
HERD THEIR LIVESTOCK FROM THE COUNTRYSIDE,
THROUGH THE TOWN TO THE MARKET.

A HUGE RANGE OF PRODUCE WOULD BE SOLD AT THE MARKETS,
FROM LEATHER, JEWELS AND CLOTH TO SPICES, SUGAR AND
FISH, PROVIDING PLENTY OF OPPORTUNITY FOR SHARP-EYED
THIEVES TO LIVE UP TO THEIR NAMESAKE.

HERALD

SWINE-HERD

OLD WOMAN

FRANKLIN

WITCH

FRIAR

HERALD

HERALDS DECLARED ANNOUNCEMENTS TO THE TOWN ON BEHALF OF THE KING OR NOBILITY. THE PEOPLE WOULD ASSEMBLE TO HEAR THE HERALD SHOUT OUT THE NEWS.

OLD WOMAN

MEDIEVAL SOCIETY WAS VERY TRADITIONAL AND A WOMAN'S ROLE IN THE TOWN WAS OFTEN LIMITED TO SUPPORTING HER HUSBAND AND FAMILY.

SWINEHERD AND PIGS

A SWINEHERD WAS RESPONSIBLE FOR LOOKING AFTER PIGS, FEEDING THEM AND CLEARING OUT THE MANURE, WHICH WOULD BE USED ON THE FIELDS.

FRANKLIN

A FRANKLIN WAS A LANDOWNER WHO WAS NOT A MEMBER OF THE NOBILITY. AS A FREE MAN, HE DID NOT OWE ANY RENT OR MILITARY SERVICE TO THE MONARCHY.

WITCH

IN MEDIEVAL TIMES WITCHCRAFT WAS FEARED THROUGHOUT EUROPE, AS PEOPLE BELIEVED IT WAS ASSOCIATED WITH DEVIL WORSHIP. IF ACCUSED OF WITCHCRAFT, THE SUSPECT WAS FORCED TO CONFESS AND WAS HUNG OR BURNT ALIVE.

FRIAR

THE CHURCH WAS CRITICISED FOR ACCUMULATING HUGE AMOUNTS OF WEALTH. MEDIEVAL TOWNS WELCOMED THE SIMPLE FRIARS WHO WENT FROM PLACE TO PLACE DELIVERING SERMONS AND BEGGING FOR SHELTER AND FOOD.

CRAFTSMEN LEARNED THEIR TRADES FROM THEIR FATHERS
OR WORKED AS APPRENTICES DURING THEIR YOUTH. THEY
OFTEN SPECIALISED IN ONE PARTICULAR CRAFT, BECOMING
MASTERS OF THEIR TRADE, SELLING WARES TO THEIR FELLOW
TOWNSPEOPLE OR THOSE OF HIGHER CLASS.

THE FEAST OF FOOLS WAS AN EXTRAVAGANT FESTIVAL WHERE THE STRICT ORDER OF THE MEDIEVAL TOWN WAS REVERSED FOR ONE DAY. A MOCK BISHOP OR POPE WOULD BE CHOSEN AS THE LORD OF MISRULE AND INVITED THE TOWNSPEOPLE TO SING, DANCE AND GENERALLY CAUSE MISCHIEF.

DURING THE FEAST OF FOOLS, THE NORMAL 'RULES' THAT
DICTATED SOCIAL HIERARCHY WERE SUSPENDED, WITH HIGH
AND LOW OFFICIALS SWAPPING PLACES. THIS FESTIVAL, HELD
AROUND 1ST JANUARY, EVENTUALLY DIED OUT IN THE SIXTEENTH
CENTURY AFTER HEAVY CONDEMNATION FROM THE CHURCH.